I LOVE MYTHOLOGY
Gods and Heroes

Text: **Anastasia D. Makri**

Illustration: **Nikos Maroulakis**
Iulios Maroulakis • **Akis Melachris**

Translated from Greek into English
Kiriaki Papakonstantinou
BA English Language & Literature / MA Psycholinguistics / DIPTRANS - DPSI
Chartered Linguist (Translator) / Translators - Interpreters Trainer
Member of the Chartered Institute of Linguists in London

UNDER THE AEGIS OF

 United Nations Educational, Scientific & Cultural Organization

ΟΜΙΛΟΣ ΓΙΑ ΤΗΝ UNESCO ΝΟΜΟΥ ΠΕΙΡΑΙΩΣ & ΝΗΣΩΝ
CLUB FOR UNESCO OF THE DEPARTMENT OF PIRAEUS & ISLANDS
Petrou Ralli 210 & Thiseos 1 Nikea,
Tel.: 210 4967757, Fax: 210 4944564 - www.unescopireas.gr e-mail: unescop@otenet.gr

AGYRA
publications

Η παρούσα έκδοση, Σεπτέμβριος 2014

The
Olympians

Ancient Greeks believed that gods lived in a shining palace on top of Mount Olympus, the highest mountain in Greece, where they observed people from. The Olympians were enormous in size and more beautiful than humans.

Ancient Greeks believed their gods were almighty, immortal and could do miracles, they lived in joy, eating ambrosia – the divine food – and drinking nectar, the wine of the gods. But just like humans, gods had their strengths and weaknesses as well. They loved, hated, and fell passionately in love! They would stand by people, but when they were angry with humans, they punished them harshly.

The Olympians were twelve, however, there were also lesser gods called demigods.

Zeus (Jupiter)

Zeus was King of humans and gods. He controlled the lives and fate of humans and held the thunder in his hands; for this reason he was called Thunder-Striker. He was also called Cloud-Gatherer because he stirred up the clouds and caused rain to fall upon the earth. People imagined him sitting on a throne made of gold and ivory, with a thunderbolt in one hand and his scepter in the other. Zeus had two jars containing good things and bad things which he dispensed to mortals, depending on their behavior. However, both gods and humans feared his rule. Zeus was also the god of hospitality.

Hera

Hera was the wife of Zeus and Queen of the Olympians. She was beautiful and majestic, sitting on her throne next to Zeus, crowned with sunbeams. She was holding a pomegranate in her hand and had peacocks at her feet, symbols of her pride and beauty.

3

Hera was the most respected of all goddesses and people used to build altars and temples in her honor. Her favorite city, Argos, honored her most. But when Zeus, her husband, loved other women, so much was her rage that she had an urge to avenge.

Athena

Athena, the favorite daughter of Zeus, was born fully armed from his forehead. And that's how the story goes...

Zeus mated with beautiful and wise Metis. Yet, there was an oracle[1] saying that Metis would give birth first to a daughter and then to a son, who would become ruler of gods and humans. On hearing such an oracle, Zeus got anxious and rushed to ask the advice of Gaia and Uranus, on what to do. "Swallow your pregnant wife before she gives birth to your child" was their advice. Zeus immediately followed their words and swallowed his pregnant wife. But when the time had come the child to be born, the pains of childbirth were driving Zeus crazy. He immediately called for his brother Hephaestus and asked him to open up his head with an ax. So, the goddess of wisdom, Athena sprang fully armed, with helmet and spear.

Athena was the patron goddess of Athens, which was

1. **Oracle:** the place where people communicated with gods seeking for advice as well as the answer/advice given by the priest or priestess to people concerning their future.

named after her. She offered Athenians the olive tree, which is the symbol of peace and they built the Parthenon and celebrated the Panathenean festival in her honor.

Poseidon (Neptune)

Poseidon was the god of the sea, earthquakes and horses and second in power after his brother Zeus. He lived less on Mount Olympus and more into the sea depths. With his trident in hand and a herd of dolphins following him, he loved wandering around the sea. When he was angry, he struck the water with his trident and a giant tidal wave would come rushing. Poseidon was also called Earth-Shaker because when the he stirred up the sea with his formidable trident, the earth trembled and shook.

His wife was Amphitrite, the daughter of Oceanus. Poseidon gave the horse to the humans, who honored him organizing horse races at the festivals called Poseidonia.

Demeter

Demeter was the goddess of earth, grain and fertility. She did not stay long on Olympus because when Pluto, the god of the Dead, fell in love with her daughter, the beautiful Persephone, Demeter wandered around Greece with a torch in hand, to find her. She reached the Palace of King Keleos at Eleusis. There, she was welcomed with great joy and the goddess, in order to repay their hospitality, taught them how to cultivate wheat and grains and how to tame wild animals. The people of Eleusis held the Thesmophoria festival and the Eleusinian mysteries in honor of her.

Demeter, desperate for not finding her daughter, threatened Zeus to barren the earth, so that people would die of hunger. Then Zeus talked to Pluto and they agreed Persephone to stay in Hades for four months and with her mother for the rest eight months of the year.

Hermes (Mercury)

Hermes was the son of Zeus and Maia, daughter of Atlas. He was born in a cave on the Kyllini Mountain. From an early age his brilliance was evident. He was the messenger of the Olympians and the god of profit and commerce. He was called wing-legged because he was wearing winged sandals and cap, to fly swiftly.

When he was young, he created the first lyre from a tortoise shell. Later, he went to Pieria where he stole Apollo's cattle and brought them to Pylos. Zeus intervened to reconcile the two brothers. All ended well. Hermes offered his lyre to Apollo, and Apollo let him keep his oxen.

6

Apollo

Apollo was god of the Sun, Prophecy and Music. He was the most beautiful son of Zeus and the mortal beauty Leto. He was also the twin brother of goddess Artemis.

When Hera found out about Leto, chased her and she fled to the island of Delos, where she gave birth to her twins. So, Delos became the sacred island of ancient Greeks. Apollo was also worshiped at Delphi, where there was the famous oracle. There, Pythia gave people the oracles informing them about the will of the gods.

Artemis

Artemis, the goddess of hunting, carried a bow and a quiver of arrows, but she was not involved in wars. She was a peaceful goddess, who loved animals and spent most of her time in the countryside, surrounded by the nymphs. The deer and the bear were her symbols. She also protected women who had difficult childbirth.

When she was a young girl, she told her father, Zeus, that she did not want to get marries, as she preferred to run free on the mountains and valleys.

Ares (Mars)

Ares was the god of war. He was the son of Zeus and Hera and always ready for war. The people dreaded him and they never honored him with sacrifices. Even his father, Zeus, was not much fond of him because he was always involved in quarrels and fights.

Eris was Ares' sister, who the god of war always took with him to sow discord. Ares fought with the Trojans against the Greeks. His wife was the most beautiful Aphrodite. She had chosen him as her husband instead of lame Hephaestus, whom she was forced to marry. The union of Ares and Aphrodite gave birth to Harmony.

Aphrodite (Venus)

Aphrodite was the most beautiful of all goddesses. She suddenly risen from the foam of the waves close to Cyprus; that's why she was also called Kyprogeneia.

She was the goddess of beauty, love and protector of the orphans and girls. Her first husband was unsightly

Hephaestus, but later she married Ares, and they had a beautiful baby boy, Eros. People loved her dearly and built beautiful temples in her honor.

Hephaestus

Hephaestus was the god of fire and blacksmiths, son of Zeus and Hera, who was so ugly by birth that his mother kicked him away only to land on the island of Lemnos. As he fell to the ground, he broke his leg and was lame. There, on Lemnos, he set up his smithery and manufactured ironware and weapons for the gods. Actually, he was the one who made the arms of Achilles.

Hestia

Goddess Hestia was respected and highly appreciated by ancient Greeks. In fact, her statue was put by the fireplace. She was the most modest of the single goddesses and the protector of home and family. She lived on Olympus guarding the palace of the gods. People first made their sacrifices to Hestia and then the other gods.

Pluto and Dionysus

We have seen the twelve Olympians, the twelve major gods. However, there was also the god of the underworld, Pluto or Hades, as well as Dionysus, son of Zeus and princess Semele. Merry Dionysus, wreathed in ivy and vine branches, was the god of grapes and wine. He liked to live near people and feast with his friends, the Nymphs.

The labors of Hercules

Hercules, the famous hero, was the son of Zeus and Alcmene, wife of Amphitryon, King of Tyrins. The goddess Hera was very jealous of Hercules, because he was a child of her husband with another woman. So, determined to get rid of him, one night she sent a pair of poisonous snakes in his crib. Hercules, however, was already so strong that grabbed the snakes with both his hands and strangled them.

As years went by, Hercules became a very strong young man. Hercules was a friend of Thespius, King of Thebes. The Thebans had to pay an annual heavy tax to the kingdom of Orchomenos. That year, however, Hercules managed not only to drive away the tax collectors but also to help Thebans defeat their army. The king of Thebes was so excited that he gave Hercules his daughter Megara for a wife. Hercules and Megara had three beautiful sons.

The jealousy of Hera, however, was more and more flaring up and decided to cast a spell on him to lose his mind. As a result, confused and angry, Hercules killed his own sons. When he realized what he had done, he was hopeless and got locked in his room, without any food and water for days. One day, he went off to the oracle of Delphi[1]. Apollo's oracle[2] told him that to be redeemed he would have to serve for ten years Eurystheus, King of Tiryns – a canny little man – who would assign him twelve labors. If Hercules performed them successfully, the gods would forgive him for what he had done.

Labor 1

The Nemean Lion

The first labor assigned by King Eurystheus was to kill the Nemean Lion, which terrorized the whole region. Hercules was looking for the lion for days. One night he heard roaring – it was the terrible lion. Hercules immediately sent out his arrows. But the lion's skin was so tough that it was not

---

1, 2. **Oracle:** the place where people communicated with gods seeking for advice; oracle is also the answer or advice given by the priest or priestess to people concerning their future.

even scratched. Then, Hercules picked up his club and went after the lion with all his strength. The lion was punchy and so Hercules managed to immobilize it and crush its neck. After that, he took the flayed skin and wore it, pulling the dead lion's head over his own, as a helmet. Seeing him, the king was almost dead with fear. When he came round, he assigned Hercules as his second labor to kill the Lernean Hydra.

Labor 2

The Lernean Hydra

The Hydra was a monstrous serpent with nine heads full of poison. This beast lived in the swamps near a place called Lerna. Hercules this time did not go alone, but took with him his trusty nephew, Iolaus. Once they reached the swamp they waited for a while, but the Hydra would not appear. Then Hercules took the arrows out of his quiver, lit them up and shot the flaming arrows at the dry reeds. Soon the whole place burst into flames. Suddenly, the angry monster jumped out of its den and run at

Hercules. He grabbed his sword and started cutting off the serpent's heads. However, in the place of each head cut two new ones grew. Then Hercules set fire to his spar and attacked the monster once more. The moment he cut one head, Ioalus burnt the wound on the headless neck, so as no new heads would grow. Finally, the Hydra fell dead. The moment Hercules returned to Eurystheus, the king assigned the next labor - to capture the wild boar that lured on Mount Erymanthos.

Labor 3
The Erymanthian Boar

This boar had tremendous strength and destroyed everything in its path. It was hard for Hercules to trace it

14

because the mountain was high and steep. But, when he found the boar, he chased it for several days and finally managed to exhaust the animal and carried it alive on his shoulders, to Mycenae. Once King Eurystheus saw the beast, he hid again in his jar frightened. When the king came round, he assigned Hercules with his next labor.

Labor 4
The Hind of Ceryneia

The fourth labor of Hercules was to catch a female deer with golden horns, which was the favorite pet deer of goddess Artemis. A whole year Hercules was trying to catch it, but in vain – until one day, near the river

15

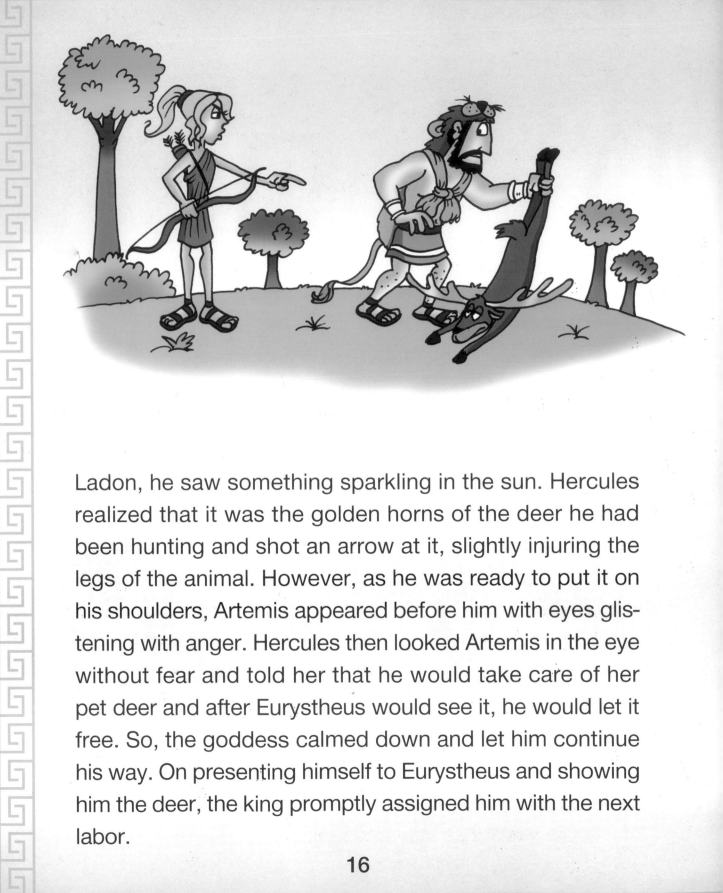

Ladon, he saw something sparkling in the sun. Hercules realized that it was the golden horns of the deer he had been hunting and shot an arrow at it, slightly injuring the legs of the animal. However, as he was ready to put it on his shoulders, Artemis appeared before him with eyes glistening with anger. Hercules then looked Artemis in the eye without fear and told her that he would take care of her pet deer and after Eurystheus would see it, he would let it free. So, the goddess calmed down and let him continue his way. On presenting himself to Eurystheus and showing him the deer, the king promptly assigned him with the next labor.

Labor 5
The Augean Stables

Hercules' fifth labor was to clean Augeas' stables within a single day. Sun, Augeas' father, had given his son so many livestock flocks that the shepherds did not have enough time to clean up the stables; as a result an unbearable odor emerged in the whole area. Hercules realized that, in order to perform this labor, except his hands he had to use his brain as well. So, he dug wide trenches to two rivers, Alfeios and Peneus, which flowed nearby. Then, he turned the course of the rivers into the trenches. The water rushed through the stables, flushing them out into the sea. Hercules was successful once more.

17

Labor 6
The Stymphalian Birds

The sixth labor was to kill a flock of terrible birds: the Stymphalian birds which devoured animals – sometimes even people. Their beaks and wings were made of iron and lived in the Lake Stymfalia. Hercules brought with him two bronze cymbals, a gift of goddess Athena to his aid. On reaching the lake, he started clashing them loudly. The birds, terrified by the noise flew out of their hiding place and Hercules started shooting them with his arrows. The birds that escaped Hercules' arrows flew away for good.

Labor 7
The Cretan Bull

When Hercules went back to King Eurystheus, he brought him one of the birds he had killed. The king

did not hesitate and assigned him the next labor, which was to catch the great white bull which belonged to Minos, the King of Crete. When Hercules got to Crete, King Minos welcomed him and when heard the purpose of his visit, he said that the bull was a very wild animal that killed people and devastated the whole island. Once Hercules found the bull in an olive grove, he tried to ride it, but the beast saw him and run on him. Fire was coming out of its nostrils. Hercules caught him by the horns. The bull struggled, but in the end collapsed exhausted on the ground. Hercules arrived at Mycenae crossing the Aegean Sea on the back of Minotaur. Eurystheus, on seeing the bull, was terrified once again and immediately assigned Hercules as the next labor to catch and bring to him the man-eating horses of King Diomedes.

Labor 8
The Man-Eating Horses of Diomedes

The kingdom of Diomedes was in Thrace. This time, Hercules took four of his friends with him. The king wel-

19

comed them warmheartedly, but Hercules had no confidence in him. He told his companions that they had to get the horses and leave that very evening. However, Diomedes sensed what they were about to do and chased them with his soldiers. He should

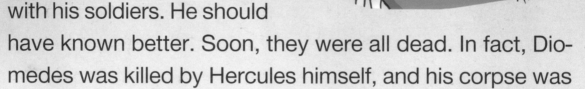

have known better. Soon, they were all dead. In fact, Diomedes was killed by Hercules himself, and his corpse was fed to the horses. As they were no hungry anymore, the four horses obeyed Hercules who harnessed them to the chariot of Diomedes and riding the wind.

Labor 9
Hippolyte's Belt

As his next labor King Eurystheus ordered Hercules to bring him the belt of Hippolyte, Queen of the Amazons. The Amazons were fierce women warriors that nobody dared to pit against. Hercules took a few companions with him; Theseus, Telamon and Peleus were among them. On arriving at the kingdom of the Amazons, they were amicably welcomed. When Hercules told all-beautiful Hippolyte that he came to get her belt, she looked at him with deep admiration and was ready to take it off and give it to him. Goddess Hera was full of envy that Hercules would succeed once more. Disguised as an Amazon warrior, Hera told the Amazons that Hercules was going to carry off their queen. It was then that the massacre started. The Amazons run at Hercules and his companions and the battle started for good. In the end,

Hercules was fighting head to head with Hippolyte, until the queen defeated gave him her belt, to let her free. Then, the companions got together and exhausted took their way back.

Labor 10
The Cattle of Geryon

Hercules, however, had no time to rest. Eurystheus immediately ordered him to find Geryon, the three-headed caveman and fetch his cattle. Geryon lived on an island near Africa and had a dog with two heads and a serpent tail, called Orthus. The trip was long and tiring. The god Sun felt sorry for Hercules and gave him a goblet to use like a boat. Hercules found Geryon on arriving at the island, but before he could get his cattle, he was attacked by the wild dog. Hercules bashed it with his club so hard that it fell dead at once. Then, Geryon was shot dead by Hercules' poisonous arrows. The hero put the cattle in the goblet boat and headed to the palace of Eurystheus.

Labor 11
The Apples of the Hesperides

The next labor assigned to Hercules was to fetch Cerberus, the guarding dog of the underworld. It was a very difficult labor. Fortunately, Hermes and Athena showed him the way and after a long and grievous journey, they reached the holy waters of the Styx. There they found Charon, who sailed them to Hades. Pluto, the lord of the Underworld, was not glad at all to hear the reason of Hercules' visit. However, Hercules promised to look after his dog and Pluto allowed the hero to get the monster with him. Cerberus was standing at the gate of the underworld. It had three heads, each one with a mane of snakes. The

beast attacked, but it had to submit to the force of the hero, and Hercules brought it to Eurystheus.

Labor 12
The Cerberus

Ten years had passed by... The last labor assigned to Hercules was to bring him three golden apples from the tree of the Hesperides, which was located at the edge of the world. There, the giant Atlas was holding up the sky on his shoulders. When Hercules arrived, he asked Atlas to help him. Hercules had first to kill the guardian-dragon of the tree and then come back to Atlas. Hercules found the dragon, killed it and then returned to Atlas, who told him that only he could take the apples from the tree. Hercules took the sky on his shoulders, so that the giant could

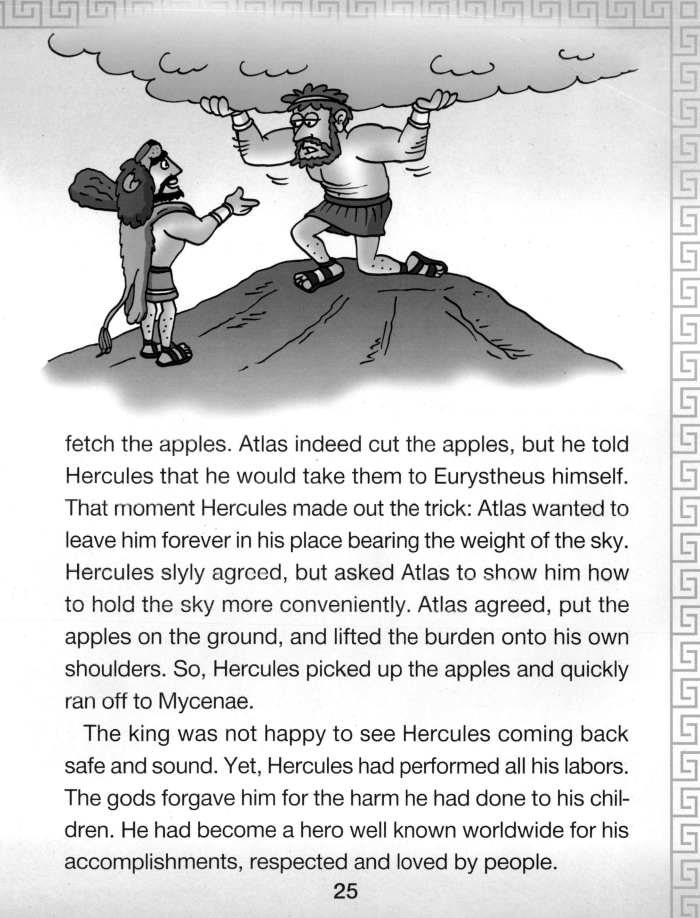

fetch the apples. Atlas indeed cut the apples, but he told Hercules that he would take them to Eurystheus himself. That moment Hercules made out the trick: Atlas wanted to leave him forever in his place bearing the weight of the sky. Hercules slyly agreed, but asked Atlas to show him how to hold the sky more conveniently. Atlas agreed, put the apples on the ground, and lifted the burden onto his own shoulders. So, Hercules picked up the apples and quickly ran off to Mycenae.

The king was not happy to see Hercules coming back safe and sound. Yet, Hercules had performed all his labors. The gods forgave him for the harm he had done to his children. He had become a hero well known worldwide for his accomplishments, respected and loved by people.

The labors of
Theseus

Aegeus was one of the first kings of ancient Athens. He was fair and his people loved him; however, he was longing to have children of his own.

In one of his trips to Peloponnese, he arrived at Troezen. There, he met the beautiful Aethra, daughter of King Pittheus, and married her. Aethra soon got pregnant by Aegeus and, when he heard the news, the king of Athens was very happy.

But the time had come for Aegeus to return to Athens, where his first wife waited for him. He took his beloved Aethra to the Temple of Zeus Sthenios (the Strong). There, Aegeus hid his sword and pair of sandals under a rock and told Aethra: "My dear, if our child is a boy, when he becomes a young man, bring him here. If he is strong enough to lift the rock and take the sword and sandals, then along with them send him out for Athens to find me and I'll recognize him".

A few months later, Aethra gave birth to a beautiful boy, named Theseus, and everyone in the palace rejoiced.

The Journey of Theseus

Theseus grew up into a handsome strapping young man. He admired Hercules very much and wanted to be like him.

Time had come when Aethra took him on the hill and showed him the rock. Theseus lifted it without much difficulty and found the sandals and the

27

sword. He put on the sandals and girded on the sword. Then Aethra hugged him goodbye and told him to go to Athens to find his father, who was waiting for him.

The robber Periphetes

Theseus set off on his journey, all too happy. Pittheus, his grandfather, advised him to sail there because the road on land was full of robbers. Theseus, however, did not follow his grandfather's advice.

People were proud of Theseus and throughout his journey they came to welcome him. Eventually, he arrived at Epidaurus. There, in a dark forest, lived the vicious robber Perphtetes, son of Hephaestus, who urged people to come near him and then killed them with an iron club, the Coryn.

When he saw Theseus, he ran at him in order to kill him. But Theseus, after a hard struggle, managed to kill him the same way as the robber killed the passersby. Then he continued his journey to Corinth.

The robber Sinis

When Theseus arrived at the Isthmus, he was attacked by the robber Sinis, who was terrorizing the whole region. He was also called Pityocamptes, meaning the one who bends the pine trees. He fastened the feet of his victims on the tops of two pine trees and bent them only to release them later to tear the passersby apart.

Theseus fought him with all his strength and managed to kill him, hitting the robber on the head with his club.

Then, he fastened him to a pair of pine trees – in the same way the robber fastened his victims – and so Sinis had the same horrible death.

Suddenly, Theseus heard a cry behind the brushwood. It was Perigoune, Sinis' daughter. Theseus, who felt sorry for her, soothed her and promised that he would protect her forever. Then, happy continued his journey.

The robber Sciron

Theseus reached Athens. When he arrived at Crommyon – currently Agii Theodori region – he killed the monstrous Sow of Crommyon, a huge female boar that destroyed the villagers' crops. Then, he arrived at the Scironian Cliffs, at the Kakia Scala region. There lived another terrible robber, Sciron, who after robbing his victims ordered them to wash his feet. As they bent down, he gave them a kick into the sea, where they were eaten by a giant wild tortoise.

When Theseus saw the robber, rushed and fought with him. In the end, he managed to throw him into the sea where the giant tortoise devoured him with pleasure.

31

The wrestler Cercyon

Theseus was near Eleusis, when suddenly a huge man, the wrestler Cercyon, appeared in front of him. This giant compelled passersby to wrestle with him until he killed them.

Theseus, once more, did not flinch and fought bravely, until he lifted the huge man high and then threw him down to his death. So, the hero managed to clear the path from the villain Cercyon.

The robber Procrustes

When Theseus arrived at Iera Odos, near Dafni, he found Procrustes, a robber who tortured passersby to death. After robbing them, he forced all travelers to lie on a bed. If they were too long, he sawed out parts of their body to make them fit and if they were too short, he

pulled their legs to become longer, until they came apart. When Procrustes saw Theseus asked him to give him what he had, but the hero grabbed him and killed him in the same way he killed his victims. After that, Theseus felt great relief.

Theseus arrives at the palace

Theseus continued his way until he reached Kifissos River. There, he washed to purify himself of the killings he had committed. Then we was dressed, girded on his sword and headed for the palace of Aegeus. The king, who had heard so much about his accomplishments, honored and welcomed him with pleasure. But once he noticed the sandals and sword, he realized that the young hero

was his son. All too proud, he introduced him to the Athenians, and appointed him his successor.

Theseus had heard of a bull that was destroying the crops in Marathon. So, he decided to extinguish the beast and save the residents. He caught the bull and sacrificed it to the gods.

Theseus kills the Minotaur

That year, king Minos would send for seven young men and seven young women, who the Athenians had to give him as a tax for the death of one of Minos' sons, who had been killed while participating in the Panathenaic festival.

Minos, therefore, fed the young victims to the Minotaur, a monster half a bull and half a man locked in the Labyrinth, a maze dungeon, of which no one ever managed to get out alive.

Theseus decided to take the place of one of the young

men and go to Crete with them. The sails of the ship were black. Before sailing off, Aegeus asked Theseus if all ended up well, to raise white sails

on return. "This way, son, I will know that you are coming back alive".

With the help of Ariadne, Minos' daughter, who fell in love with him, Theseus managed to kill the Minotaur and get out of the Labyrinth alive.

The death of Aegeus

Theseus with Ariadne and his companions sailed off to Athens. However, they stopped at the island of Naxos,

to rest. On their way to Athens, they did not get Ariadne with them, and let her sleep on the beach, because god Dionysus did not let them. Theseus, full of joy that they were all going back home safe and sound, forgot to change the sails.

So Aegeus, who anxiously waited for his son's return every day at Sounion, seeing the ship coming back with black sails threw himself into the sea.

Theseus, on hearing of his father's death was devastated.

Theseus becomes King of Athens

The Athenians, although they mourned for the death of Aegeus, welcomed Theseus with great honors and proclaimed him king.

The first thing Theseus did as a king was to unite all the

municipalities of Athens into a big city. Indeed, he established every four years the Great Panathenaic festival, a celebration of great sport events and religious ceremonies for the Athenians to honor goddess Athena and remember the union of all municipalities.

Theseus ruled his people for many years in wisdom and justice.

Theseus and the Amazons

The Amazons had their own kingdom in the region of Pontus, which they ruled without any man. They were fearsome warriors and everybody was intimidated by them. Theseus, who was good friend with Hercules, fought against them and won them. One of the Amazons, Antiope, fell in love with Theseus and followed him to Athens. There he gave birth to his son, Hippolytus.

But then, the Amazons attacked the Athenians and were defeated. Antiope was killed in the battle.

Theseus and Phaedra

Later on, Theseus married Phaedra, the other daughter of Minos. Phaedra fell in love with Hippolytus, who refused her love and then she killed herself in despair. However, she left a note to Theseus, accusing his son for not respecting her.

Theseus believed Phaedra's accusations, cursed his son to find a horrible death and expelled him. As Hippolytus was leaving on a chariot to Peloponnese, the horses suddenly ran wild. The chariot was crushed and the boy was killed.

Shortly afterwards, the truth was revealed, but it was too late.

The end of Theseus

Theseus, embittered, abandoned Athens and along with his friend, Pirithous, wandered about, trying to get married with daughters of gods. They went to Hades to seize

Persephone, but Pluto, the lord of the underworld captured them. Hercules freed Theseus but on his return to Athens, he found another king on his throne. The Athenians had proclaimed Menestheus a king. Theseus, embittered once more, left to his estates, on the island of Skyros.

39

There, his friend Lycomedes was king, who from fear of losing his throne to Theseus, one day invited the hero to show him his kingdom from a hill. There he pushed Theseus off the cliff putting an inglorious end to the life of a great hero.

Jason and the golden fleece

Jason was the grandson of the first king of Iolcus, Kritheas. His father was Aeson and his mother the nymph Tyro. Jason was still an infant when his uncle, Pelias, usurped the throne from his father, Aeson. To protect Jason, his father sent him away to the mountains where he grew up under the care of the wise Chiron. Chiron was a centaur, half-man and half-horse. Chiron tutored Jason several things; among others to be honest and generous.

When Jason had come of age, Chiron revealed his true identity and which his origin was.

"It's time to go back home and claim what belongs to you", told him Chiron.

So, Jason set out to Iolcus determined to take the throne back. On his way he came across the Anavros River, on the bank of which a withered old woman was sitting.

"Will you help me across, lad" she pleaded. Warm-hearted Jason did not think twice. Taking the old woman on his back, he set off into the current. Yet, in his effort he lost one of his sandals. "Don't worry, lad, this is a

good sign. I'll stand by you in everything you need", said the old woman, who was none other than goddess Hera in disguise, revealing herself to Jason on that far shore.

Both surprised and pleased by this meeting, Jason went on his way. A few days later, he arrived in Iolcus and went straight to the palace. On seeing him, his uncle Pelias was terrified. Gods had warned him that one day young man "who wears but a single sandal" would take his throne.

"I know why you are here, Jason. Yet, to give you my throne, you should first bring me the golden fleece", said

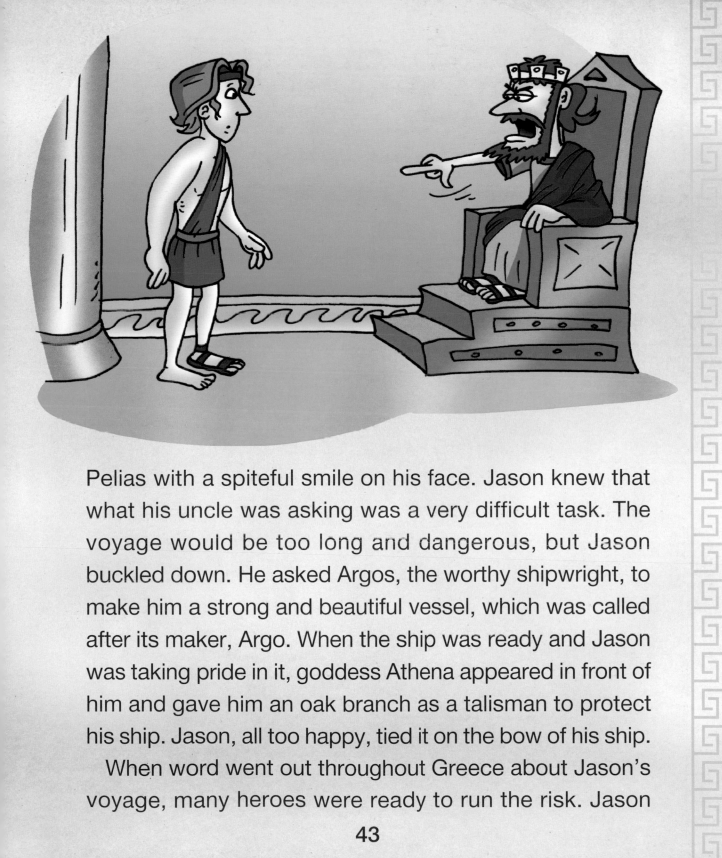

Pelias with a spiteful smile on his face. Jason knew that what his uncle was asking was a very difficult task. The voyage would be too long and dangerous, but Jason buckled down. He asked Argos, the worthy shipwright, to make him a strong and beautiful vessel, which was called after its maker, Argo. When the ship was ready and Jason was taking pride in it, goddess Athena appeared in front of him and gave him an oak branch as a talisman to protect his ship. Jason, all too happy, tied it on the bow of his ship.

When word went out throughout Greece about Jason's voyage, many heroes were ready to run the risk. Jason chose about fifty men. Among them were Orpheus, the greatest of all musicians, brave Hercules, Calais and Zetes, the winged twin sons of Boreas and Oreithyia, as well as Dioscuri, Castor and Pollux, the twin sons of Zeus. These were known as the Argonauts, after their ship. Thus, one morning they got supplies and set off in their ship. With the help of gods, tail winds helped the ship sail off.

The Adventure Begins

The Argonauts made their first stop at the island of Lemnos. There, something unprecedented happened – there were no men on the island. It seems that the women of Lemnos, for some reason, did not like men. However, goddess Aphrodite saw to the Argonauts were welcomed to the island. In fact, their hospitality was so warm that the travelers almost forgot the purpose of their voyage.

After the island of Lemnos, the voyage got really trying. They came across stormy seas and had to stop for supplies in places inimical, with hostile inhabitants. They had even to fight with wild beats; yet, they face all ordeals bravely and continued their voyage always tireless.

When they reached the land of bebryces, they met King Amycus. This savage king challenged all visitors to a boxing match and as he was so fearsome he always killed his opponent. So, once more he called out and the one who immediately accepted to fight was Pollux, the champion boxer, Castor's twin.

"Like hell you will win me! You seem rather to be tired of your life", said Amycus with an ironic laughter.

Pollux remained cool and as he was very agile and trained he managed, after a long fight, to shatter him with a severe blow. Then Jason and the Argonauts flew to their ship to avoid the rage of bebryces.

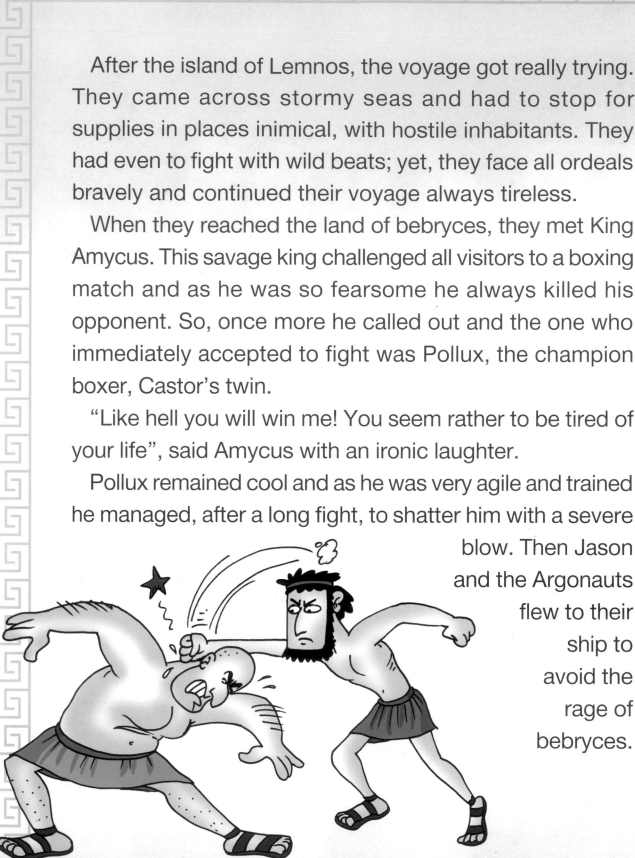

46

The Harpies

The next stop of the Argonauts was a city in Thrace. There lived the blind seer Phineus who, punished by the gods, could not eat because his food was snapped by Harpies – monsters featuring the body of a bird and the head of a woman. The Argonauts wanted his advice on how to continue their voyage. Phineus told them: "I will help you, but first you have to save me from these horrible creatures that do not let me eat".

As soon as Phineus sat to eat, the Harpies rushed to snap his food. Then, Calais and Zetes, the twin sons of Boreas, fell on them with wings on their feet and swords in their hands. Soon, no Harpies were left.

Phineus thanked them for their help and told them that the greatest danger just ahead was the Symplegades or Clashing Rocks, two enormous rocks which clashed together upon any ship passing between them. So, he advised them what to do: "Have a dove with you. When you arrive there, let it go. If it flies between the rocks in safety, then you can do it too".

The Symplegades

Once the Argonauts arrived at the entrance to the Black Sea, where the Semplegades stood, Jason set the dove free. She managed to pass safely before the rocks clashed, only losing some feathers of her tail. As soon as the rocks rebounded Jason yelled: "Hurry up! To the oars! Let's pass now!"

However, there was head wind. Then, the goddess Athena sent a huge wave that pushed Argo; thus she suffered only a splintered stern.

Their journey continued peacefully until, before arriving in Colchis, they were attacked by the Stymphalian birds. Then the Argonauts started violently beating their poles on their shields. The clangor scared the dangerous birds away and thus the heroes were saved.

Shortly after that, they arrived in Colchis. They had a rest and the following morning Jason set off to meet King Aeetes. When he arrived at the palace, he was supposedly warmly welcomed by King Aeetes himself. Jason explained that he wanted the Golden Fleece to reclaim his throne from his uncle. "I'll give it to you", said Aeetes, "but first you'll have to yoke to the plough two fire-breathing bulls with brazen feet, and sow the teeth of the dragon".

Jason was listening to him carefully wondering how he could manage to perform all these tasks...

While Aeetes was speaking, his daughter Medea was standing by his side. The moment she saw Jason she fell in love with him and decided to help him.

Being a powerful sorceress, she made a magic potion and went to Jason in the middle of the night. On seeing her he was astonished. "Jason, smear your body with this magic potion and nothing can hurt you. On sowing the dragon teeth, giants will sprout. Then, throw a big stone among them and as they fight trying to find out who threw it, you will have the chance to kill them".

The next day, Jason gathered up all his courage and went to the field to anticipate the fire- breathing Bulls, who hit the ground with their bronze hooves. Everything around was burning but Medea's magic potion was protecting Jason. Thus, he managed to grasp the two bulls from the horns and have them harnessed. All spectators remained speechless. Then, Jason plowed the field and sowed the dragon teeth.

What happened then was something very strange and scary at the same time: immediately fully-armed fierce warriors sprang out.

Jason following Medea's advice took a very big stone and threw it among them. They started fighting accusing each other. Then Jason grasped the opportunity to kill them one by one.

The Argonauts were thrilled by such a victory; and so was Medea. Yet, the latter tried to hide her excitement, for fear her father suspected his daughter had helped Jason.

Then Jason went to Aeetes and asked the Golden Fleece. Unable to believe Jason's achievement, the king promised to give him the fleece the next day. Yet, other plans were in his mind; he was planning to send his soldiers burn the Argo and kill the Argonauts.

The next day, when Jason asked the Golden Fleece of Aeetes, he refused to give it to him. Jason and the Argonauts were enraged.

Then Medea, who knew her father's plans, met Jason secretly at night and told him he had to leave immediately, but before that she would help him get the Golden Fleece.

"But how will we pass the dragon who never sleeps but remains awake at the trunk of the tree?" asked Jason. "Don't worry about that. I'll take care of it", answered Medea.

Indeed, when they reached the huge oak they saw the horrifying dragon that looked like an enormous snake. On seeing them, the dragon started hissing, showing his teeth. Then, Medea approached him murmuring some strange spells, and sprinkled over him a sleeping potion which she had prepared. It was not too long before the dragon fell asleep. Then Jason climbed up the tree, seized the Golden Fleece and hastened with Medea to his ship.

"I got the golden fleece. Hurry up! Prepare the ship. We are sailing off!" Jason cried out to his companions.

While the Argonauts were preparing the ship, Medea ran to the palace to get with her little brother, the Apsyrtos.

Before dawn, Argo had already sailed well off the harbor. On hearing the news, Aeetes commanded his ships to chase them. They were about to reach the Argonauts when Medea had a horrible idea. She killed her brother and threw his body into the sea. When Aeetes saw Medea throwing her brother's lifeless body into the sea burst into weeping unable to believe his eyes. He immediately halted his ships and commanded his men to take Apsyrtos aboard. In all this turmoil, Argo managed to sail away. After what had happened, Aeetes could not find the courage to continue chasing the Argonauts...

Zeus, however, enraged by Apsyrtos' murder sent a terrible storm which found them in the Adriatic Sea and drove the Argonauts off course. Then Athena sent them a message that in order to be purified from sin of murder they had to visit the sorceress Circe, sister of King Aeetes and Medea's aunt. Indeed, once

they reached the island of Circe and met her, they explained the reason for their visit. Then Circe sacrificed a heifer to the gods and sprinkled Jason and Medea with its blood to wash away the sin. "The gods have forgiven you. You can go now", told Circe and they sailed back home after thanking her.

When they reached Iolkos, Jason immediately went to his uncle Pelias and showed him the Golden Fleece. Then he, unable to do otherwise, gave him the throne; thus. Jason eventually became a king.